Cowee Sam
and the Swift Water Rescue

By Claire Suminski
and Annie Suminski

This book is dedicated to our
"Sapphire Auntie", Marilyn Ann Gallup Matriccino Van Tassel
and our "Amethyst Auntie", Kay Lora Gallup Kuebler who are
precious and shining gems in our family.

First Edition
ISBN-10: 0-9793869-9-2
ISBN-13: 978-0-9793869-9-2

Library of Congress Control Number (LCCN): 2016959904

Published by Red Press Co., Inc.

Redpressco.com

Sam jumps into the churning water and starts to swim towards the approaching Log.

Cowee Sam to the
Rescue!

Chapter 1

The Storm

Distant thunder booms and Cowee Sam watches over the herd of goats as they move towards the hay shed. He barks loudly as big drops of water start to fall on the ground, and the chickens and hogs once again head for cover. Sam's normally white coat is covered with mud. Farmer Joe's wife, Ruby, hears Cowee Sam's bark and knows that he is doing his job keeping the farm animals protected. It has been raining hard off and on for five days now. Farmer Joe and his daughter, Jamy, are stationed with part of their Swift Water Rescue Team up river in the Cullasaja Gorge, ready to help anyone in need.

All of the water from high up in the gorge is causing the Cullasaja River to run at full capacity, and after joining with the Little Tennessee River down in the valley, it is running high and even overflowing the banks in some places. Teams of rescue workers stand by, ready to make sure their neighbors are out of harm's way. Logs and other large debris are being swept down both rivers, and some of the back roads are washed out. Today was supposed to be the last day of rain, but it will take awhile for the rivers to calm down and get back to normal.

Serving Macon County and the Cowee Valley Area

NIKWASI NEWS

World - Business - Finance - Lifestyle - Travel - Sport - Weather

Issue: 240104   THE WORLDS BEST SELLING NATIONAL NEWSPAPER   Est - 1965

First Edition   Monday 5th June

Rescue Workers Stand By as the Little Tennessee River Overflows

Teams of rescue workers are standing by to make sure their neighbors are out of harm's way. The Cullasaja River is running at full tilt and overflowing it's banks. Logs and other large debris are being swept down the river _____ are being swept away. Swift Water Rescue workers are _____ er of the mighty water. We urge the community to

Chapter 2
Safe and Warm

Safe and warm in the main house of Cowee Mountain Valley Farm, Ruby Franklin and her granddaughter Annie are riding out the storm in another way. As the wind and rain swirls outside, the rich and sweet smell of blueberry pie baking in the oven fills the air.

Aunt Molly's Famous Blueberry Pie Recipe

Mema's Flakey Vinegar Pie Crust
(Dough makes enough for top and bottom crust)

1. Cut in (with two knives, a pastry cutter, or your fingers)
   3 cups of flour, 1 1/2 cups of shortening, and a pinch of salt
2. Beat in bowl:
   5 Tbs. of water, 1 Egg, mix well then add
   1 Tbs. of Apple Cider Vinegar
3. Add Vinegar mixture to flour
4. Form into two balls and then roll them out onto wax paper.
5. Place one in pie tin and save the other to make top crust.

Blueberry Filling

1. In a large bowl combine the following:
   6 cups of Blueberries, 3/4 cup of Sugar, 1 tsp. of Lemon zest,
   2 tsp. of LemonJuice, a pinch of fresh ground nutmeg,
   and 3-4 Tbs. of Minute Tapioca (best if ground up in grinder or food processor).
2. Add the Blueberry mixture to the dough-lined pie plate.
   Make a lattice top crust and then trim and crimp the edges.
   Brush with egg white and sprinkle with sugar.
3. Bake at 400 degrees for 15 minutes then at 350 degrees for 45 minutes

Check out the pie making pictures in the back of this book!

Ruby leans over the kitchen island and carefully rolls out enough dough to make two more pies. Her eight-year-old granddaughter, Annie, sits on the stool next to her and quietly sorts through a big bowl of fresh-picked blueberries, pulling out the ones that are not up to standard. Whenever Annie encounters an extra big blueberry, she pops it in her mouth and tastes the fresh mountain goodness.

Ruby places the bottom crusts in the pie tins, pats them in place with her fingers, and then wipes her hands on her brightly-colored apron. She smiles at her granddaughter and says, "Annie, we are so happy to have you here for a month of your summer vacation. You just arrived last night and we are already making your Aunt Molly's Famous Blueberry Pie! But I can't help notice you seem unusually quiet. Are you missing your Dad and Mom?"

Annie shakes her head as she looks up at her grandmother, one big tear rolling down her cheek.

"Grammy Ruby, I miss Cozy. He was the house dog here at the farm for as long as I can remember. When I was little, he would let me climb on his back and ride him like a horse until he got tired. Then he would just lie down and let me cuddle him like a pillow. This is my first time at the farm without him."

Ruby takes Annie's hand in hers, leans over, and kisses her cheek.

"I miss him, too. He was always good company when your Grandpa was out on rescue calls. I miss his quiet, steady ways. Say, do you remember the scripture over the fireplace?"

Casting all your care
upon him, for he careth
for you.
1 Peter 5:7

Annie glances above the fireplace and reads along as Ruby continues,

"It is 1 Peter 5:7 'Casting all your care upon him: for he careth for you.' Sometimes tough things happen in life, but just continue giving your cares to God. He will always take care of you!"

Annie hugs her grandmother tightly.

"Thank you Grammy Ruby."

Chapter 3
Heading Home

Just then, the emergency radio goes off and Farmer Joe's voice booms loud and clear,

"The storm is clearing up in the Cullasaja Gorge, and Jamy and I just finished our shift at the Dry Falls Command Post. We are heading home!"

Ruby asks Farmer Joe, "Did you have to evacuate the folks on Turtle Pond Road?"

"Yes, the road washed out and our Swift Water Rescue team helped transport the families to the shelter at the base of the gorge. There is a lot of debris in the river. I'll tell you more when I get home. Annie, is there pie in the oven?"

"Yes, Grandpa, and it smells great. Yours are in the oven now and we are just finishing up the ones to bring to the emergency shelter."

11

About an hour later, the rain has stopped and Farmer Joe and his daughter, Jamy, pull into the driveway with all of their gear and Jamy's kayak strapped down on top of the truck. Cowee Sam's ears perk up as he hears the familar red truck and runs the length of the fence along the road to welcome them home.

Ruby and Annie hurry out onto the porch as the truck comes to a stop. Annie runs down the steps to hug her Grandpa and her Aunt Jamy and to help them put away their rescue gear in the paddle shack down by the river.

Farmer Joe notices that, although the rain in the valley has stopped, all of the mud-laden water and debris from several days of rain up in the gorge has made its way down to the Cowee Valley. Parts of the Little Tennessee River bank are flooding throughout Cowee Mountain Valley Farm. Farmer Joe opens the gate to the pasture and calls to Sam, telling him to come down by the river.

Jamy and Farmer Joe still have on their wet suits. Jamy is carrying her kayak over her head. As they approach the paddle shack, it is hard to hear above the roaring of the water tumbling through a narrow section of the river just up stream from the shack. Suddenly, Sam's ears perk up. Farmer Joe says, "What is it boy?"

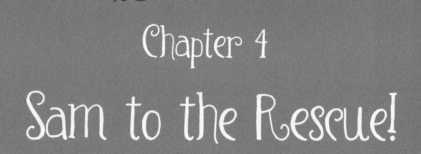

Chapter 4

Sam to the Rescue!

Sam starts racing upstream, with his eyes on a log that just shot between two boulders. On top of the log is a shaggy little black and white dog, clinging for her life! Sam jumps into the water and starts swimming towards the approaching log. It is all happening so fast! All Farmer Joe and his family can do is watch and pray! Sam makes it to the log and the little dog jumps on his back, grabbing Sam's collar with her teeth. But, can Sam make it back to the shore?

Annie yells, "Go Sam, go !"

Chapter 5
Rescuing the Rescuer

Without hesitation, Jamy straps on her helmet and jumps into the rushing current with her kayak, paddles, rescue rope, and carabineer clipped to the boat. This is what she has been trained to do. She is ready!

Ruby runs into the house to get some quilts and towels. Farmer Joe and Annie run along the edge of the river, watching for anything that might help with the rescue. Around the next bend, they spot a huge flat rock, known as Martin's Landing, angling down into the water.

Farmer Joe gives a sharp whistle to signal to Jamy and points towards the edge of Martin's Landing. If Jamy can help Sam out of the current and to that rock, both dogs might be saved. It is clear that Cowee Sam is tiring, and his head keeps going underwater from the weight of his passenger. Jamy overtakes the dogs and grabs the exhausted pup. Placing her on her lap, she clips the carabineer onto Sam's collar. Then, she paddles as hard as she can towards Martin's Landing, towing Sam behind the kayak.

Chapter 6
Martin's Landing

Farmer Joe runs to the edge of the great rock and throws a rope to Jamy. She grabs the rope, and Farmer Joe reels them in, pulling the nose of the kayak up into Martin's Landing. Ruby and Annie are cheering!

Jamy hops out, handing the little dog to Annie to wrap in a quilt. Annie holds the little dog close to warm her up. Farmer Joe unclips Cowee Sam's rope from the kayak and starts to pull Sam up onto the landing. Sam puts his front paw up on the mighty rock, but every muscle is weary from the rescue. He falls back into the river and starts to sink below the surface.

Quickly, Jamy and Farmer Joe reach down, grab Sam's collar and pull his head above water. They get Sam up on the rock and lay him down on one of Ruby's quilts. He is lifeless.

The family gathers around Sam and prays. Ruby puts another warm quilt on top of their beloved dog, as Farmer Joe kneels down next to Sam to give him CPR. He has done this before by blowing into a dog's nose, but never on his own dog.

25

The little black and white dog perks up and gives a quick bark, as if to say, "Come on Sam!!" All of a sudden, Sam's upper body jerks and water shoots out of his mouth. He shakes off the quilts and stands on all four legs! Ruby says, "Thank you God!" Everyone cheers, and the little dog barks.

Sam, courageous and true, has risked his own life to save the little dog. The sun comes out from behind a cloud and shines on a large patch of yellow buttercup flowers all around them. Annie puts her arms around the little dog and Sam and hugs them both tightly. The flowers seem to shine so brightly that Annie has an idea. She whispers in Sam's ear, " Thank you Cowee Sam for rescuing 'Buttercup' ".

Chapter 7
The Celebration

Suddenly, Jamy says, "I'm starving! Let's get out of these wet clothes and warm up by the fire with some hot chocolate and blueberry pie!" Annie asks her Grandpa, "The dogs too?" Farmer Joe answers, "This celebration would not be complete without the dogs!"

God will take care of you

A few minutes later, they are all snuggled in front of the fire and giving thanks to God for the rescue, for the food and for His care. The little dog wiggles right in the middle of the family. She clearly belongs. Grammy Ruby starts softly singing, "God will take care of you, through every day, in every way, God will take care of you" and everyone joins in for the last phrase, God will take care of you!

Farmer Joe pats Sam on the head and says, "We needed a house dog, and it looks like Cowee Sam brought us a little dog that fits right in." Jamy says, "Buttercup, welcome to our family!" And Annie exclaims, "What a great rescue!"

31

Celebration Hot Chocolate

Ingredients: (Serves 6)
1/3 cup of Sugar
6 Tablespoons of Unsweetened Cocoa Powder
(We recommend Ah!Laska Bakers Cocoa Non-Alkaline)
6 Tablespoons of Water
6 Cups of Milk
1/2 Teaspoon of Vanilla
1/2 Teaspoon of Cinnamon

Directions:
1. Combine sugar, cocoa, and water in small saucepan. Bring to boil over medium heat, stirring constantly.
2. Add milk and heat to serving temperature. Do not boil.
3. Add vanilla and cinnamon
4. Serve in mugs and top with whipped cream or marshmallows
5. Drink with friends and family rejoicing and celebrating with thankful hearts.

Glossary

Approached (Verb) to come near or nearer to someone or something.

Apron (Noun) a protective item of clothing worn over the front of one's clothes and tied in the back.

Bank (Noun) the land alongside or sloping down to a river or lake.

Bend (Noun) a curve, especially a sharp one.

Boomed (Verb) to say in a loud, deep, resonant voice.

Boulder (Noun) a large rock.

Carabineer (Noun) a coupling link with a safety closure.

Cares (Noun) an object of concern or attention.

Celebration (Noun) event or occasion of enjoyable social activity to mark one's happiness.

Clinging (Verb) to hold on tightly to.

Company (Noun) the condition of being with other people, especially in a way that provides friendship and enjoyment.

Cove (Noun) a small sheltered bay.

CPR (Noun) an emergency lifesaving procedure that is done when someone's breathing or heartbeat has stopped.

Cuddle (Verb) to hold close in one's arms as a way of showing love or affection.

Current (Noun) a body of water moving in a definite direction.

Debris (Noun) loose natural material consisting especially of broken pieces of rock.

Distant (Adjective) far away in space or time.

Emergency (Noun) a serious, unexpected, and often dangerous situation requiring immediate action.

Encounter (Verb) to unexpectedly experience.

Entrance (Noun) an opening that allows access to a place.

Evacuate (Verb) to remove someone from a place of danger to a safe place.

Folks (Noun) people.

Gorge (Noun) a narrow valley between hills or mountains, typically with steep rocky walls and a stream running through it.

Hauled (Verb) to pull or drag with effort or force.

Jerked (Noun) a sudden quick movement of the body.

Kayak (Noun) a canoe made of a light frame with a watertight covering having a small opening in the top to sit in.

Kitchen Island (Noun) an unattached counter in a kitchen that you can get to from all sides.

Knelt (Verb) to be in a position in which the body is supported by a knee or knees.

Laden (Adjective) heavily loaded or weighed down.

Lifeless (Adjective) lacking vigor, vitality, or excitement.

Narrow (Adjective) of small width.

Nose (Noun) the front end of a boat, car, or other vehicle.

Notices (Verb) to become aware of.

Overflow (Verb) to flood or flow over.

Overtook (Verb) to come upon.

Paddle (Noun) a short pole with a broad blade at one or both ends used to move a small boat or canoe through the water.

Paddle Shack (Noun) a place to store all kayaking gear such as paddles and lifejackets.

Passenger (Noun) a traveler other than the driver, pilot, or crew.

Pasture (Noun) land covered with grass and other low plants suitable for grazing animals.

Peak (Adjective) greatest or maximum.

Perk (Verb) to become lively, cheerful, or vigorous.

Racing (Verb) moving swiftly.

Rack (Noun) a framework, typically with rails, bars, hooks, or pegs, for holding or storing things.

Recipe (Noun) a set of instructions for preparing a particular food item.

Rescue (Verb) to save someone from a dangerous or distressing situation.

Rich (Adjective) Pleasantly deep or strong.

Rounded (Verb) to pass and go around something.

Rushing (Adjective) done with excessive speed.

Sandbar (Noun) a long narrow sandbank.

Scripture (Noun) the writings found in the Bible.

Sharp (Adjective) having a strong or piercing sound.

Shelter (Noun) a place giving temporary protection from bad weather or danger.

Shore (Noun) the land along the edge of a sea, lake, or other body of water.

Shot (Verb) to move suddenly or rapidly in a particular direction.

Signal (Noun) a gesture, action, or sound that is used to convey information or instructions.

Standard (Noun) a level of quality.

Steady (Adjective) firmly fixed, supported, balanced.

Sturdy (Adjective) strongly and solidly built.

Swept (Verb) to push or move someone or something with great force.

Swift (Adjective) happening quick.

Towing (Verb) to pull something or someone behind something else.

Transport (Verb) to take or carry people or things from one place to another by means of a vehicle, aircraft, or ship.

Tumble (Verb) to move or rush in an uncontrolled way.

Unusually (Adverb) not common or ordinary.

Upstream (Adverb) against the current.

Vacation (Noun) an extended period of recreation.

Valley (Noun) a low area of land between hills or mountains, typically with a river or stream flowing through it.

Waded (Verb) to walk through water.

Washed Out (Idiom) to erode something away.

Weary (Adjective) feeling or showing tiredness.

Wetsuit (Noun) a close-fitting garment made of neoprene or similar material typically covering most of the body, worn for warmth in water sports or diving.

Writing Your Own Family Stories

Many parts of this book are rooted in real life stories that took place on our hobby farm. Farmer Joe and Jamy Beth really do have Swift Water Rescue training and work as weekend rafting guides for Nantahala Outdoor Center. Jamy Beth is out paddling rivers in her kayak every chance she gets. They have many stories to tell.

One of the best dogs we ever had just showed up on our porch one day and never did leave for fifteen years. We think he was somehow separated from his family, because of a storm. We tried many different things to find his family without result. Each day we became more attached to him. He had adopted us and we adopted him too. He is the "Cozy" in the beginning of this story.

Farmer Joe is a volunteer Fireman. One day he answered a call and a house was on fire. The family was huddled outside, crying not because their house was on fire, but because their family dog had succumbed to smoke inhalation. Farmer Joe knelt on the ground next to the dog and decided to try canine CPR. He cupped his hands around the dog's snout and blew into his nose. After a while the dog started to breathe again and jumped to his feet wagging his tail. The folks lost their home, but were crying tears of joy because their beloved dog was alive!

Our family's first response in real life is to look to God with great confidence in our hearts, knowing that He will take care of us. Just like in the story.
What stories do you have to share?

Your story ideas:

We would love to hear about your family! Send your story to:
Suminski Family Books
P.O. Box 1402
Franklin,NC 28744
You may receive a surprise back from us in the mail!

What to do if you find a Stray Pet:

In the Cowee Sam Series we take some poetic license. At times we may leave out details that could slow the story down and take you away from the point we are trying to make. In "Cowee Sam and the Swift Water Rescue" after Sam and Jamy rescue the dog, they take her home and Buttercup becomes a part of their household. In real life there are things that you should do if you find an animal that has been separated from its family.

#1 Be very careful around a stray animal. They may be frightened or hurt and they may not know right away that you are there to help them. Approach very slowly and let them come to you.

#2 Call your local animal shelter or animal control office. This will let them know that you have the animal, should the owners call them. They may suggest a place to go to see if the animal has a microchip that can be scanned which will reveal the owner right away.

#3 If you decide to take the animal home, keep them separate from your other pets at first. The found animal may be sick, fearful, or aggressive with other animals.

#4 Take pictures and make a found pet poster to post around the area you found the animal. You can also put these posters at Veterinarian offices, or post them on websites such as petfinder.com.

#5 A person finding a stray dog or cat does not automatically become the new owner until they have satisfied any local and/or State requirements. Check with your local Humane Society or local Animal Control Center to learn what you will need to do.

Knot Tying

Swift Water Rescuers need to know how to tie knots. All of the knots in the "Family of Eights" are very helpful to learn. This lesson will show you how to tie a basic "Figure of Eight" and a "Bowline".

1 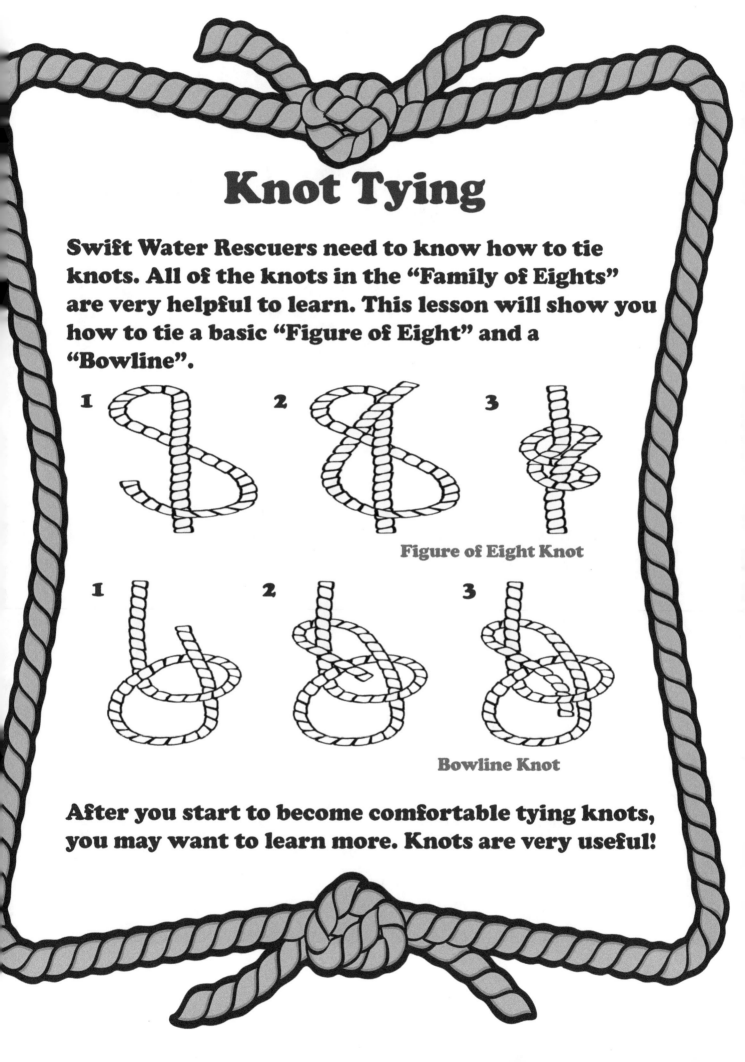 **2** **3**

Figure of Eight Knot

1 **2** **3**

Bowline Knot

After you start to become comfortable tying knots, you may want to learn more. Knots are very useful!

Making Aunt Molly's Famous Blueberry Pie

Find the Recipe on page 6

Make crust according to the recipe on page 6 and form into two balls.. Take the first ball and place on floured surface.

Roll out dough evenly into a circular shape.

Cover the dough in plastic wrap and roll the dough to transfer it into the pie plate.

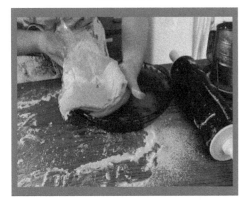

Transfer to pie plate and take off the plastic wrap.

Adjust the crust and press into plate

Brush the crust with egg whites

Gather the filling ingredients listed in the recipe on page 6.

Mix the Pie filling ingredients together

Put the filling into the Pie crust.

oll out the second ball of
gh to form the top crust.

Cut the dough into even
strips about 1 inch thick.

Lay the strips horizontally

Weave in the vertical
rips to make a beautiful
lattice crust

Crimp the edges by
pressing the dough
hanging over onto the
rim of the pie plate.

You can use any left
over dough to make
a decoration on top.

THiS pie iS
Super
deLiciouS
aNd reaLLy FUN
to MaKe and
SHare!

15 minutes

45 minutes

Bake at 400 degrees for
15 minutes
Then
Bake at 350 degrees for
45 minutes

Let cool then
ENJOY!

Brave Ol' Cowee Sam

A little shivering lonely dog
soaked and stranded on a log,
helpless against the rushing river
but then came Cowee Sam

Sam ran fast and jumped right in
the cold rough water and began to swim
the tiny dog got on Sam's back
Brave ol' Cowee Sam

Annie yell's "go Sam go!"
But will Sam make it back to the shore?

Jamy knows that Sam is drained
She paddles hard, the distance gained.
Her kayak becomes the recue boat,
For lil' dog and Cowee Sam

The little dog is safe and sound
but Cowee Sam is all but drowned
Farmer Joe knows what to do
to rescue Cowee Sam

The family gathers around to pray
For God's healing and help that day.

As Farmer Joe does mouth to snout,
Sam's mouth opens and water shoots out
He gets up fast on all four legs
And shakes the water off.

Sam came back to life that day,
Brave ol' Cowee Sam.

written by:
Eric
McQuitty

Hear this song on our website:
suminskifamilybooks.com

Fun with Limericks!

A Limerick is a 5 line poem of a humerous nature.

The first, second, and fifth lines must have seven to ten syllables (same verbal rhythm) with the words at the end of each line rhyming.

The third and fifth lines only have to have five to seven syllables (same verbal rhythm) with the words at the end of each line rhyming.

Limericks are many times written like riddles, that have a kind of twist. The answer may be revealed in the final line.

In this set of Limericks about Cowee Mountain Valley Farm, the answers are written upside down, in the blue box, at the bottom of the page after limerick #9.

Can you write a Limerick? You could also draw a picture to go with it. If you like how it turns out, we would love to see it!

Please mail it to us at:

Suminski Family Books
P.O. Box 1402
Franklin, NC 28744

You may receive a surprise back from us in the mail!

Cowee Mountain Valley Farm Limericks

1. When a storm rushes through like a blast
   This makes streams rush incredibly fast
   These water conditions
   Put some in positions
   Where they feel that their safety won't last.

2. These self powered boats can deliver
   As they're narrow and long, like a sliver
   To move, you must battle
   The waves with a paddle
   Through oceans, through lakes or through rivers

3. If you're lost in a dangerous place
   Your locale this young lady will chase
   With her friend, Farmer Joe
   On the hunt she will go
   'til she finds you, and helps get you safe.

4. Whether crunchy or meaty or sweet,
   This place grows the food that we eat
   When our bodies are nourished,
   Our minds and souls flourish
   Thanks to here, where they grow many treats.

5. Made from berries large, dark and quite sweet
   This dessert is a farm-favorite treat
   From Aunt Molly's collection
   The taste is perfection
   For old friends or new ones to meet.

6. This lady's the Queen of the farm
   While her husband saves lost ones from harm
   Grandma, caretaker,
   And yummy pie maker
   She greets all her guests with open arms.

7. While this dog started out in distress
   At the end with a family she's blessed
   Her new family gave
   Her a perilous save
   And their welcoming love was expressed

8. This granddaughter and guest at the valley
   Was helping the rescue to rally
   Then after the save,
   'twas this girl who gave
   The new dog a name right up her alley.

9. This dog is the farm's noble shepard
   He'll defend the livestock like a leopard
   He knows how to defend
   Is an excellent friend
   And with love from his family he's peppered.

Plot Points Challenge

Write the number that corresponds with the order of events next to the sentence to put the story in order. For example, write the number 1 next to the thing that happened first, a number 2 next to the thing that happened second and so forth.

Cowee Sam jumps in the water to save another dog.

Everyone warms up around the fire with hot chocolate and blueberry pie.

Farmer Joe gives Cowee Sam CPR.

Jamy and Farmer Joe come home.

Annie and Grammy make a blueberry pie together.

Jamy gets in her kayak and paddles to save Cowee Sam and the other dog.

Word Scramble Puzzle Fun!

Unscramble each of the clue words. Take the letters that appear in the boxes with circles and unscramble them for the puzzles answer.

LETTIL NESSEETEN RERVI

JYAM

OWCEE SMA

BERBUYLRE EIP

NEINA

OHT HEATOLCCO

LASLAUAJC GERGO

MYMAGR

TUTLER PNDO

ARMERF OEJ

W

Cowee Sam's Swift Water Word Search

APRON/BANK/BOULDER/CARABINEER/CELEBRATION/CUDDLE/DEBRIS/
EMERGENCY/EVACUATE/FOLKS/GORGE/JERKED/KAYAK/NOSE/OVERTOOK
PADDLE/PASTURE/RACK/RECIPE/SANDBAR/SCRIPTURE/STANDARD/SWEPT
TRANSPORT/TUMBLE/UPSTREAM/VACATION/VALLEY/WETSUIT

```
T U M B L E E V R R C P U N E
Y S E Q A P Z A A E K P J O R
C C A V I N B C L A S J T S U
U N N C N D K E Y T A N D E T
D R E E N I B A R A C E T S S
D R G A G R K E M A T R E T A
L R S O A R A V P F O U L A P
E Q E T V M E R D P I T D N V
H M I D H E O M S E J P D D A
P O T Z L N R N E E K I A A L
N E V A C U A T E G T R P R L
S K L O F R O D O R Y C E D E
S W E P T Y J B V O O S L J Y
N O I T A C A V C G K H Q F H
R T W E T S U I T S I R B E D
```

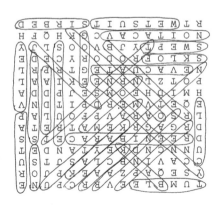

Ros Webb is a children's book illustrator. She has been illustrating children's books for close to a decade. She developed her own style as a children's book artist following the birth of her first daughter and the publication of her picture book "*The Big Sleepy Bear and the Pink Flamingos*". Ros lives in the Irish mountains and is greatly inspired by her three children, four dogs and five cats. She has worked extensively with authors from across the globe and is continually inspired by their imagination and story telling.

Afterward

This book has been a work of love, and we have had fun working together as mother and daughter. While this book is not a faithful retelling of events in our lives, it is based on some of the adventures the Suminski family has had through the years. Our family has a hobby farm, and a Bible fellowship that meets in our home and we are very involved with our community. As a result, we have many adventures to share.

In this story, Ruby encourages her family to keep their trust in God. Annie had a sad heart because the farm house dog had died. Everyone in the story had to face a scary situation when the river became dangerously fast. People have situations every day where they need help. Ruby shared a verse with her Granddaughter that was so meaningful to their family they had it framed and hung over their mantle.

1 Peter 5:7 "Casting all your care upon him; for he careth for you."

Psalm 46:1 "God is our refuge and strength, a very present help in trouble"

Sometimes tough things happen in life, but just continue giving your cares to God. He will always take care of you!

The family in this story helps each other because they love and care for each other. God is always ready to help us because He loves and cares for us.

> *1 John 4:19*
> *"We love him, because he first loved us."*

God is always ready to help when we have need! He always loves us!

> *Hebrews 4:16 "Let us therefore come boldly unto the throne of grace, that we may obtain mercy, and find grace to help in time of need."*

We hope you had fun reading this book and that you have many adventures of your own. The Suminski Family is going to keep on having adventures and there are more Cowee Sam stories on the way!
Ever thankful for God's grace and love,
Claire and Annie Suminski
April 23, 2017

> *Romans 10:9 "That if thou shalt confess with thy mouth the Lord Jesus, and shalt believe in thine heart that God raised him from the dead, thou shalt be saved."*

> *Ephesians 2:8 "For by grace are ye saved through faith; and that not of yourselves: it is the gift of God."*

Meet the Graphic Designer for the Cowee Sam Series

Susan Swedlund is an artist that lives most of the year in Beloit, Wisconsin. Recently she and her husband have been blessed to become part-time residents in Franklin,North Carolina. Susan studied and received her Art degree at Washburn University in Topeka, Kansas. Along with being a Graphic Designer Susan is a potter and owns the business Potter Sister. While in Franklin she frequently teaches classes at Cowee Pottery School. She and her husband, Glen, love seeing Cowee Sam when they walk their dog, April.

We would like to thank Raphael Albinati for his hard work and dedication to Suminski Family Books. He has laid a wonderful and beautiful foundation that we can continue to build upon.

Acknowledgements

We would like to thank Monica Collier of Red Press Co., for her publishing help, Katie Farris and Kaitie Hansen for their help on special projects, Glen Swedlund for his proof reading , Eric McQuitty for writing the song "Brave Ol' Cowee Sam" and D. Young Barton for writing the Limericks for this book.

Special thanks to the real Farmer Joe and Jamy and Jerome and Molly for their love and support.

And most of all, thanks to our heavenly Father for His goodness and love.

Katie Farris and
Kaitie Swedlund

Monica Collier

Eric McQuitty

D. Young Barton

Glen Swedlund

About the Authors

Claire Suminski lives in a small Mountain community in Western North Carolina. Her husband and four children run a family business and have built a small hobby farm together. After twenty years of Home Schooling, Claire thought it might be rewarding to share family stories and adventures with more children and help fuel in them their love of learning.

Annie Suminski is a graduate of the University of South Florida. She does bookkeeping by day and likes to weave, crochet , Contra dance, sing ballads, and read books by night.

Her Angora goats are on permanent vacation at the Cowee Mountain Valley Farm.

CPSIA information can be obtained
at www.ICGtesting.com
Printed in the USA
BVHW02s0802180818
524671BV00006B/12/P